THE
INTERNATIONAL LIBRARY
OF
PIANO MUSIC

ALBUM SEVEN

Gaston Dufy at the Piano
by Raoul Dufy, French painter, illustrator and decorator (1877-1953).
Painting of his brother by the artist.

THE INTERNATIONAL LIBRARY
OF
PIANO MUSIC

Advisory Board

LEONARD BERNSTEIN

FRANK C. CAMPBELL

VAN CLIBURN

AARON COPLAND

OLIVER DANIEL

NORMAN DELLO JOIO

ROBERT DUMM

SR. M. SOPHIE GOLDKAMP, CSJ

WALTER HENDL

PETER MENNIN

ROBERT PACE

RUDOLPH SERKIN

ROGER SESSIONS

HALE SMITH

CLAUDETTE SOREL

Editorial Staff

FELIX GREISSLE
Music Director and Editor-in-Chief

CORINNA MARSH
Literary Editor

ARNOLD BROIDO
Associate Music Editor

ELIZABETH VOLDSTAD
Assistant Music Editor

GEORGE COOKE
Copy Editor

THE UNIVERSITY SOCIETY, Inc.
25 Cottage Street,
Midland Park, New Jersey 07432

Educational Publishers since 1897

In addition to its wealth of contemporary material, this *new* INTERNATIONAL LIBRARY OF PIANO MUSIC combines the most successful teaching and playing masterpieces of its predecessors; namely:

Famous Songs and Those Who Made Them	Copyright 1896
The World's Best Music	Copyright 1897
Paderewski — Century Library of Music	Copyright 1900
Modern Music and Musicians	Copyright 1912
La Mejor Musica del Mundo	Copyright 1917
The University Course of Music Study	Copyright 1920
The International Library of Music	Copyright 1925
A Melhor Musica do Mundo	Copyright 1930
The International Library of Music	Copyright 1934
The International Library of Music	Copyright 1945
The International Library of Music	Copyright 1956

International Standard Book Number: 0-87824-053-5
Library of Congress Card Number: 68-41733 rev/M

Manufactured in the United States of America

Pub. No. 1006

TABLE OF CONTENTS

For Albums V, VI, and VII (Romantic Period)

* from Mendelssohn's *Songs Without Words*

** from Schumann's *Album for the Young, Op. 68*

** from Schumann's *Album for the Young, Op. 68*

*** from Tchaikovsky's *Album for the Young, Op. 39*

The Romantic Period

(1820—1900)

In the Village

Au Village

Modeste Moussorgsky

Larghetto, quasi fantasia

Grandioso, Meno mosso
marcato il canto

Allegretto scherzoso non troppo allegro

senza Ped.

cresc. e accel.

poco ritard.

A tempo non agitato (Alla zingara)

Poco a poco più vivo al fine. Capriccioso

Oriental Dance

Poco allegro

M. Ossokine

Minuet in Olden Style

(Menuet à l'antique)

Ignace J. Paderewski
Op. 14, No. 1

Reprinted by permission of Gordon V. Thompson Limited — Toronto, Canada

412

5-594-3

March of the Little Tin Soldiers

Gabriel Pierné
Op. 14, No. 6

Allegretto moderato

a tempo

ben staccato (senza pedale)

poco cresc.

418

Humoresque

Sergei Rachmaninoff
Op. 10, No. 5

Allegro vivace

Andante

Tempo I

Polichinelle

Sergei Rachmaninoff
Op. 3, No. 4

Allegro vivace

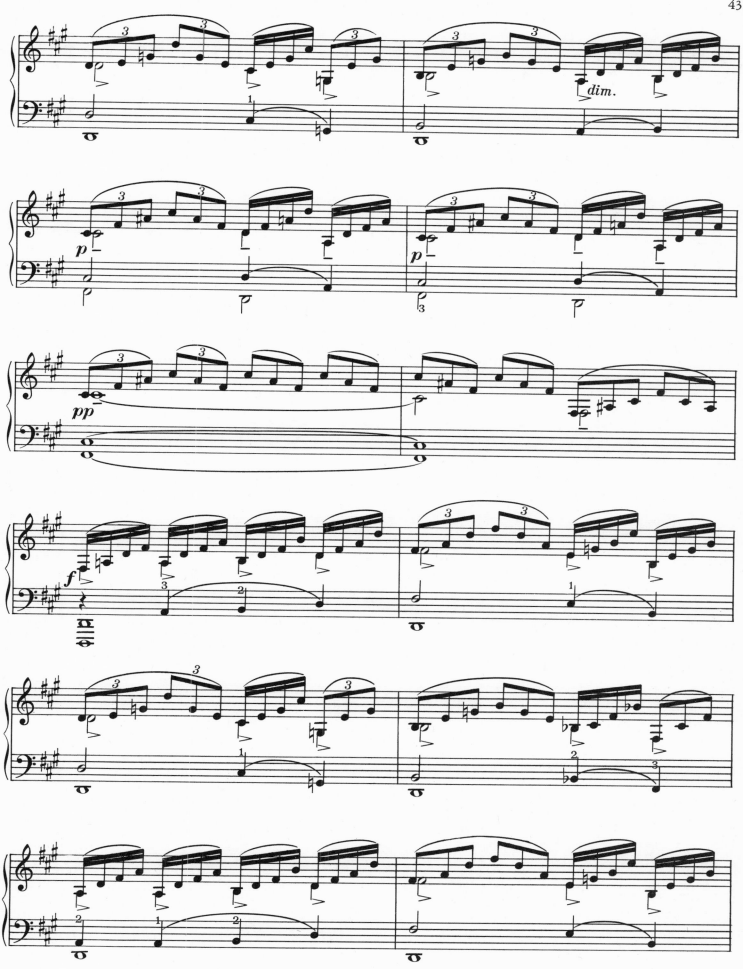

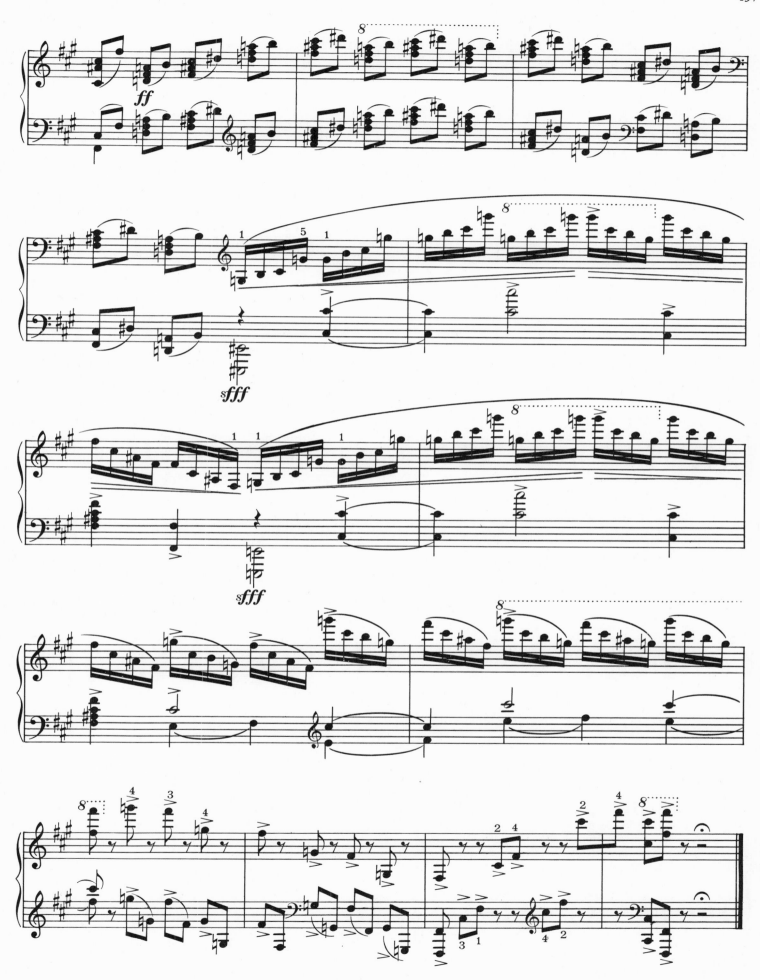

Prelude
C-sharp minor

Sergei Rachmaninoff
Op. 3, No. 2

Agitato

Prelude

B major

Sergei Rachmaninoff
Op. 32, No. 11

444

3-599-3

At the Spinet
painted in 1886 by Adolph Erdmann von Menzel (1815-1905), German
painter and illustrator.

A Monsieur A. Arensky

Sérénade

Sergei Rachmaninoff
Op. 3, Nr. 5

Sostenuto

Tempo di Valse

Polish Dance

Xaver Scharwenka
Op. 3, No. 1

Allegro con brio

Bourrée

from "Six études" for the left hand alone

Camille Saint-Saëns
Op. 135, No. 4

Des Abends
(In the Evening)

Sehr innig zu spielen
(To be played fervently)

Robert Schumann
Op. 12, No. 1

Aufschwung
(Soaring)

Robert Schumann
Op. 12, No. 2

Sehr rasch
(Very fast)

Grillen
(Whims)

Mit Humor
(With humor)

Allegro

Robert Schumann
Op. 12, No. 4

Chorale
from "Album for the Young"

Robert Schumann
Op. 68, No. 4

First Loss
from "Album for the Young"

Nicht schnell
(*Not fast*)

Robert Schumann
Op. 68, No. 16

Happy Farmer

returning home from work

from "Album for the Young"

Robert Schumann
Op. 68, No. 10

Frisch und munter
(*Gaily, with animation*)

Hunting Song
from "Album for the Young"

Robert Schumann
Op. 68, No. 7

Frisch und fröhlich
(Gaily and joyfully)

Knight Rupert

from "Album for the Young"

Robert Schumann
Op. 68, No. 12

Little Humming Song

from "Album for the Young"

Robert Schumann
Op. 68, No. 3

Nicht schnell
(*Not fast*)

Little Piece
from "Album for the Young"

Robert Schumann
Op. 68, No. 5

Nicht schnell
(*Not fast*)

Little Romance

from "Album for the Young"

Robert Schumann
Op. 68, No. 19

Nicht schnell
(*Not fast*)

Little Romance
from "Album for the Young"

Robert Schumann
Op. 68, No. 26

Nicht schnell, hübsch vorzutragen
(*Moderato grazioso*)

Little Study
from "Album for the Young"

Leise und sehr egal zu spielen
(Softly and evenly)

Robert Schumann
Op. 68, No. 14

Ped. simile

Melody

from "Album for the Young"

Robert Schumann
Op. 68, No. 1

A Piece by Robert Schumann
  etching made in 1864 by Ignace Henri Jean Theodore Fantin-Latour
  (1836-1904), French painter and lithographer. From the New York Public
  Library, Prints Division.

Norse Song

from "Album for the Young"
Greeting to G.*

Im Volkston
(*In modo popolare*)

Robert Schumann
Op. 68, No. 41

*) The Danish composer, Niels W. Gade 1817-1890.

Rustic Song
from "Album for the Young"

Robert Schumann
Op. 68, No. 20

Im mäßigen Tempo
(Moderato)

Soldiers' March

from "Album for the Young"

Robert Schumann
Op. 68, No. 2

Munter und straff
(Gaily and in strict rhythm)

The Theater is Over

from "Album for the Young"

Robert Schumann
Op. 68, No. 25

Etwas agitiert
(With some agitation)

Wild Horseman
from "Album for the Young"

Robert Schumann
Op. 68, No. 8

Winter Time

from "Album for the Young"

Ziemlich langsam
(Moderately slow)

Robert Schumann
Op. 68, No. 38

Cradle Song

Robert Schumann
Op. 124, No. 6

Papillons

Robert Schumann
Op. 2

Allegro

6

Allegro con brio

15-635-10

Allegro con spirito

11

Tempo primo

Scenes of Childhood
(Kinderszenen)

From Strange Lands and People
(Von fremden Ländern und Menschen)

Robert Schumann
Op. 15

*) The original manuscript indicates only metronome markings.

A Curious Story
(Kuriose Geschichte)

Catch Me
(Hasche-Mann)

Pleading Child
(Bittendes Kind)

Perfect Happiness
(Glückes genug)

(Allegro moderato) ♪ = 162

Important Event

(Wichtige Begebenheit)

6.

Reverie
(*Träumerei*)

At the Fireside
(Am Kamin)

(Allegretto grazioso) ♩ = 138

8.

Knight of the Rocking Horse
(Ritter vom Steckenpferd)

Almost too Serious
(Fast zu ernst)

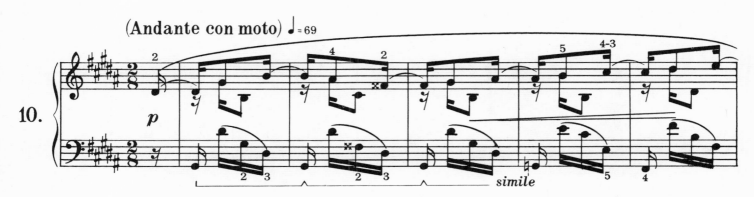

Frightening
(Fürchtenmachen)

526

Child Falling Asleep

(Kind im Einschlummern)

The Poet Speaks

(Der Dichter spricht)

Rustle of Spring

(Frühlingsrauschen)

Christian Sinding
Op. 32, No. 3

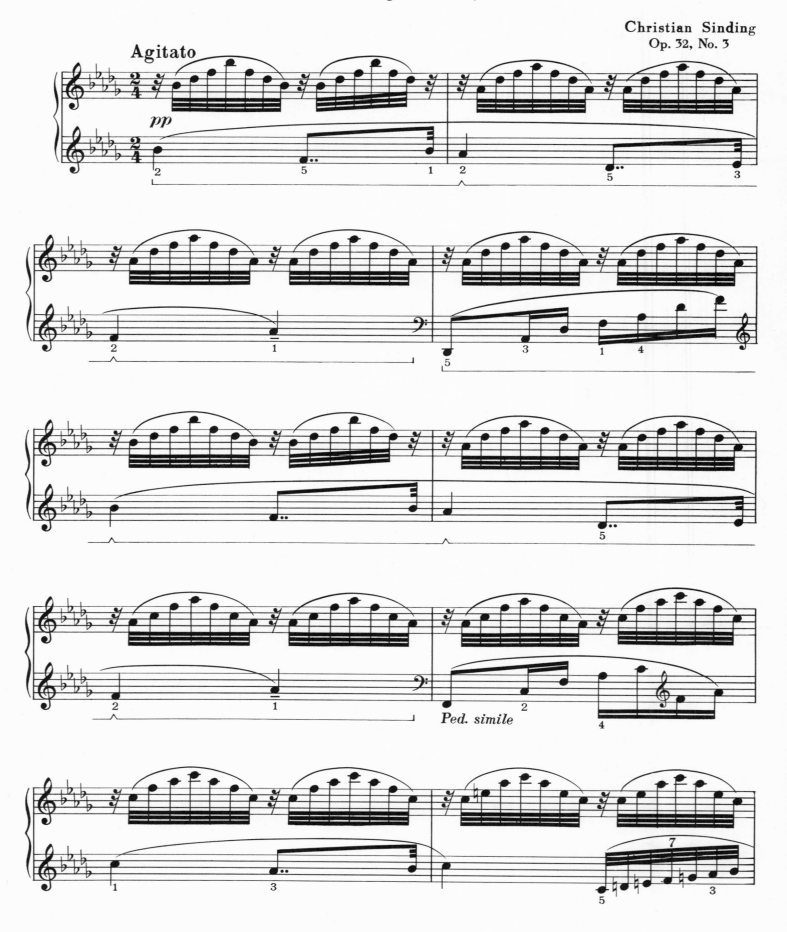

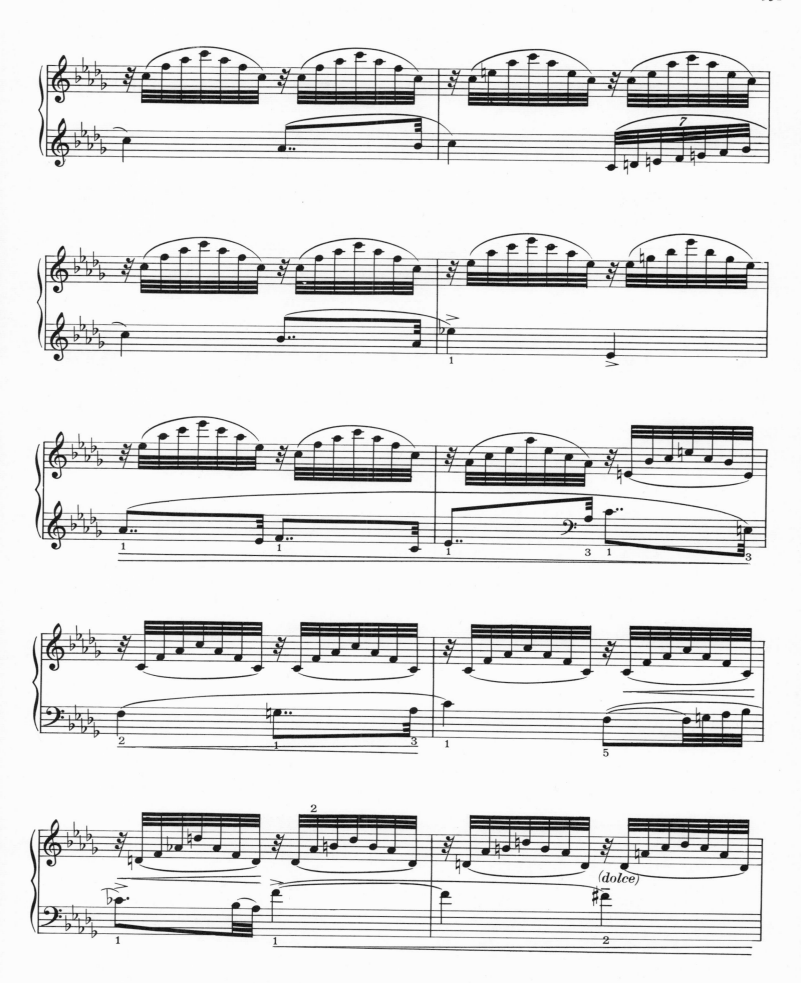

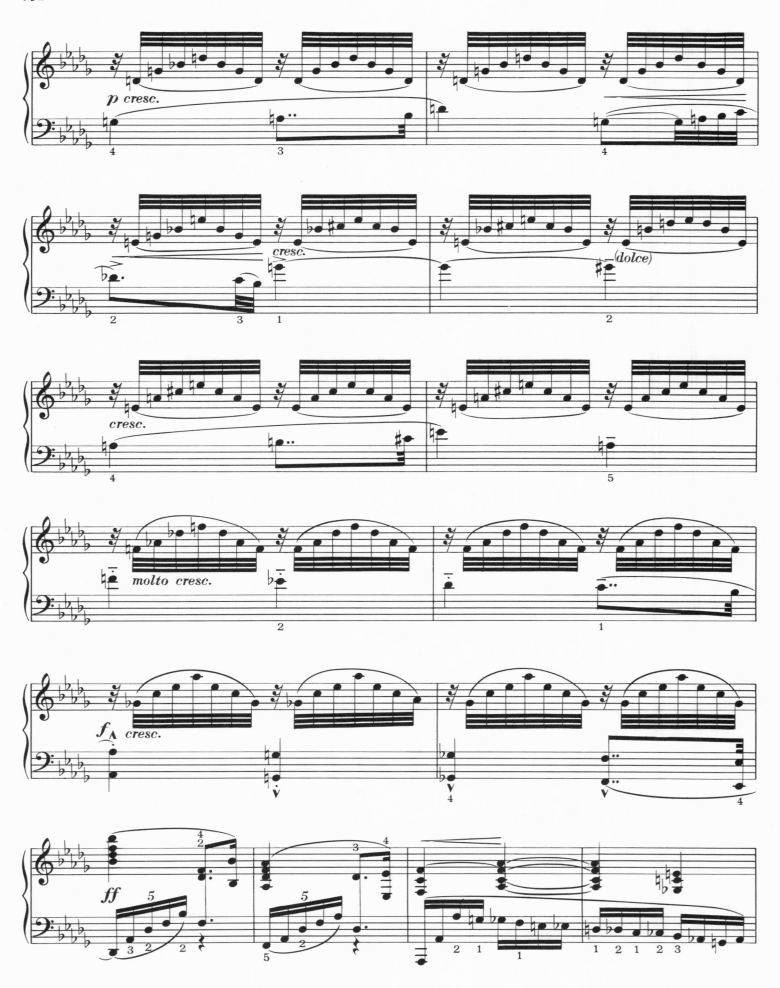

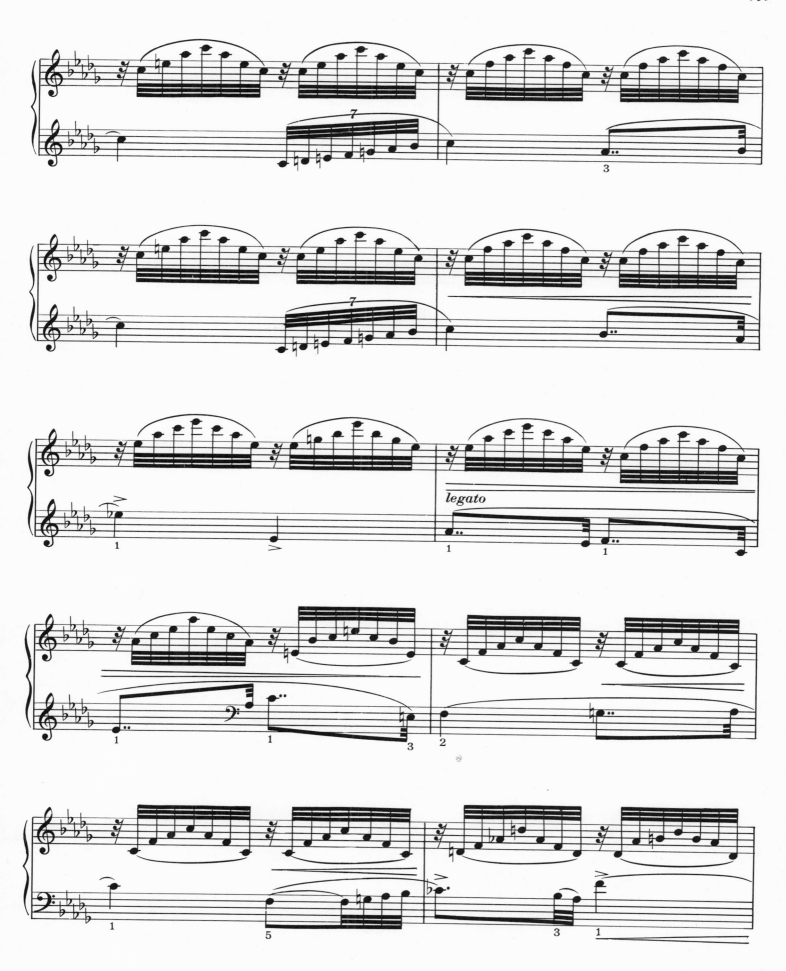

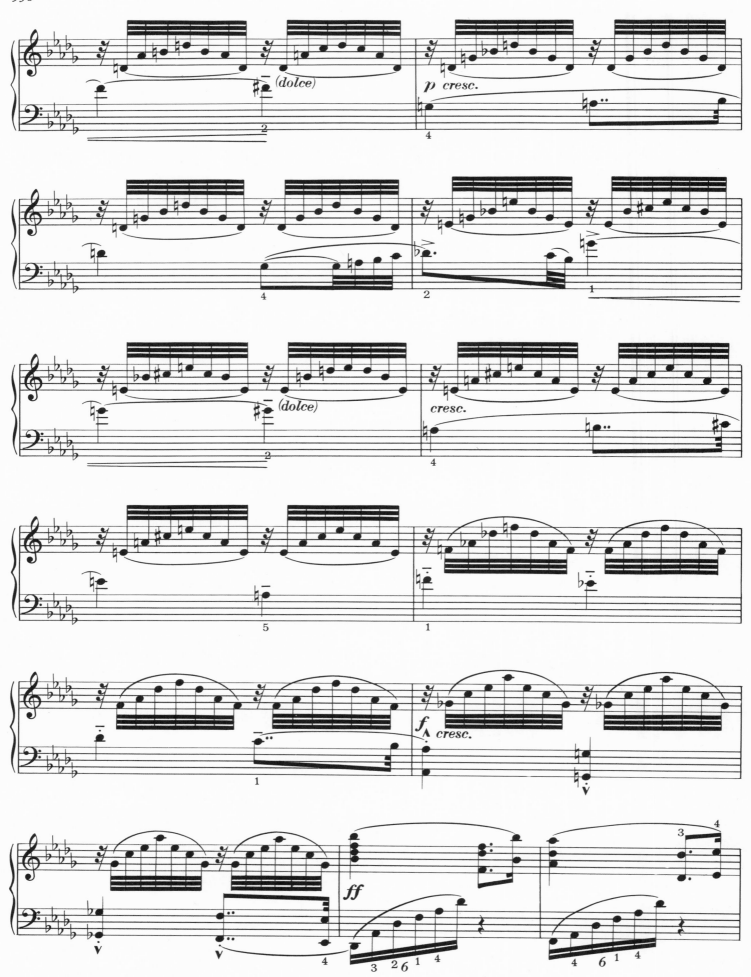

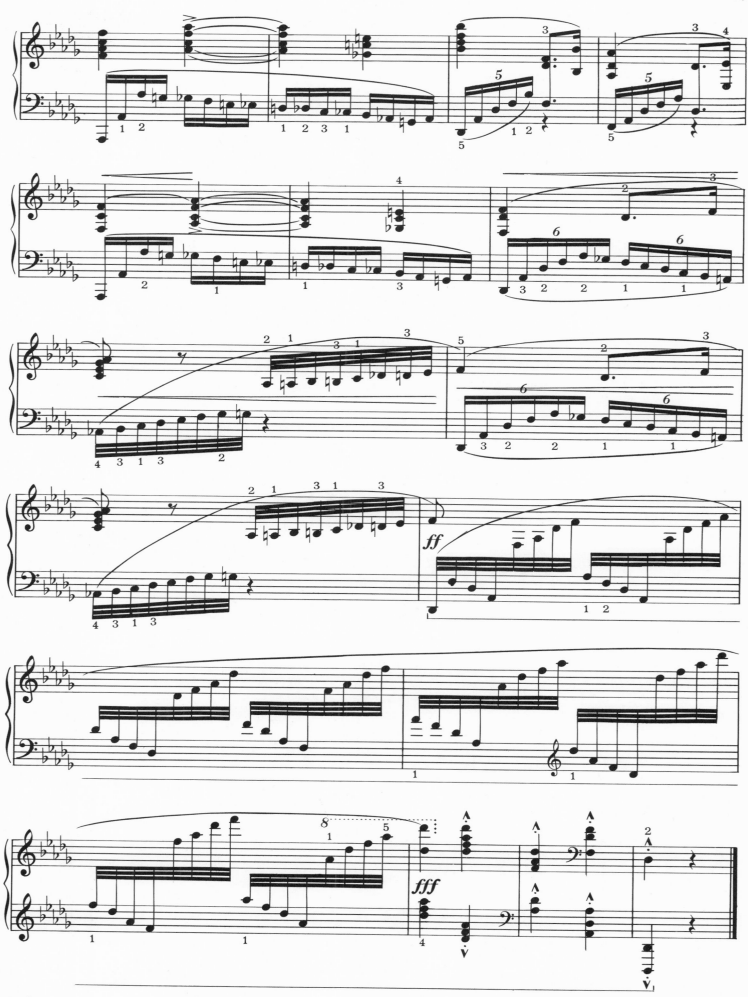

Eroticon

Emil Sjögren

Bohemian Dance
from "Album for the Young"

Peter I. Tchaikovsky
Op. 39, No. 14

The Doll's Funeral

from "Album for the Young"

Peter I. Tchaikovsky
Op. 39, No. 7

Adagio

In the Church

from "Album for the Young"

Peter I. Tchaikovsky
Op. 39, No. 24

March of the Wooden Soldiers

from "Album for the Young"

Peter I. Tchaikovsky
Op. 39, No. 5

Moderato

Mazurka
from "Album for the Young"

Peter I. Tchaikovsky
Op. 39, No. 10

Tempo di Mazurka

The New Doll

from "Album for the Young"

Peter I. Tchaikovsky
Op. 39, No. 9

A Nursery Tale
from "Album for the Young"

Peter I. Tchaikovsky
Op. 39, No.19

Morning Prayer
from "Album for the Young"

Peter I. Tchaikovsky
Op. 39, No. 1

A Brahms Fantasy
  etching produced in the early 1880's, by Max Klinger (1857-1920), German allegorical painter, etcher, and sculptor. From the New York Public Library, Prints Division.

Old French Song
from "Album for the Young"

Peter I. Tchaikovsky
Op. 39, No. 16

Molto moderato

Song of the Lark

from "Album for the Young"

Peter I. Tchaikovsky
Op. 39, No. 22

557

2-652-2

Sweet Dreams
from "Album for the Young"

Peter I. Tchaikovsky
Op. 39, No. 21

Andante con molto espressione

Waltz
from "Album for the Young"

Peter I. Tchaikovsky
Op. 39, No. 8

Russian Song
from "Album for the Young"

Peter I. Tchaikovsky
Op. 39, No. 11

Chanson Triste

Peter I. Tchaikovsky
Op. 40, No. 2

Allegro non troppo

Humoresque

Peter I. Tchaikovsky
Op. 10, No. 2

December

from "The Seasons"

Peter I. Tchaikovsky
Op. 37a, No. 12

Tempo di Valse

TRIO

CODA

March

from "The Seasons"

Peter I. Tchaikovsky
Op. 37a, No. 3

June

from "The Seasons"

Peter I. Tchaikovsky
Op. 37a, No. 6

Andante cantabile

July
from "The Seasons"

Peter I. Tchaikovsky
Op. 37a, No. 7

Allegro moderato con moto

Melody

François Thomé

Moderato, quasi valse

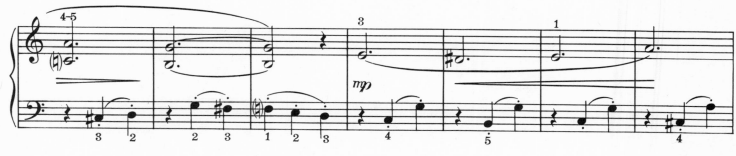

Scherzino

V. Volkoff